Nuffield Trust Report

IMPROVING THE HEALTH OF THE NHS WORKFORCE

Report of The Partnership on the h[illegible] NHS Wo[illegible]

Siân Williams
Susan Michie
Shriti Pattani

Introduction by
John Wyn Owen

Published by
The Nuffield Trust
59 New Cavendish Street
London W1M 7RD

ISBN 1-902089 07 3

Publications Committee
Sir Derek Mitchell KCB, CVO
Professor John Ledingham DM, FRCP
Mr John Wyn Owen CB

CONTENTS

ABOUT THE AUTHORS

Siân Williams MBBS, MD, MRCP, MFOM
Consultant in Occupational Medicine
at the Royal Free Hospital and School of Medicine, London
Dr Williams promotes the multidisciplinary approach to Occupational Health and combines service provision with research and teaching. Research interests include the risks to health service staff of blood exposures and their treatment. Dr Williams has previously been an Employment Medical Advisor at the Health and Safety Executive, where she gained extensive experience of industrial hazards and their prevention.

Susan Michie, B.Phil., MA, D.Phil., C.Clin.Psychol.
Senior Research Fellow in Health Psychology at the Royal Free Hospital School of Medicine and the United Medical and Dental Schools of Guy's and St Thomas's
Dr Michie is a health psychologist providing a clinical service for health care staff and students, based in the Occupational Health Unit at the Royal Free. She specialises in stress management for doctors and medical students and her published research covers both this and other areas of health service research. Dr Michie's previous post included organisational interventions aimed at preventing the causes of stress and ill health at work. Her current research, funded by the Wellcome Trust, is the study of the psychological and social aspects of the new genetics.

Shriti Pattani, MBChB, BSc, DRCOG, MRCGP
Specialist Registrar in Occupational Medicine
at the Royal Free Hospital, London
Dr Pattani joined the Occupational Health Department in January 1997. Previously she worked as a general practitioner. She is currently researching into ill health retirement among NHS staff.

INTRODUCTION

In the Secretary of State for Health's recently published *Our Healthier Nation - A Contract for Health*, issued as a Consultation Paper, the Government recognised that as people spend a lot of their time at work, healthy work places are vital to their health. The Partnership on the Health of the NHS Workforce is in this report offering a serious contribution to the Government in its leadership position in the improvement of the health of the workforce of the NHS. The Partnership's report responds to the expectation of the consultation paper, which is to protect staff from the harm that certain jobs can cause, and reflects its concern with individuals, communities and the nation at large. The report is a clear example of a partnership of organisations with a shared concern.

There is no doubt that over the next few years, a number of changes in policy and practice will be implemented to ensure that the health of those working in the health sector is improved and more effectively managed. *The New NHS* White Paper recognises the importance of establishing a new culture of openness and cooperation within the NHS, and the Partnership Report is presented in the spirit of the White Paper's commitment to the involvement of all staff in taking the recommendations of The Partnership forward.

There has been a considerable amount of research and many reports in the past on the health of those working in the NHS, particularly in relation to doctors' health. Each report pointed to concern about levels of ill health and its implications, but none was sufficiently extensive or robust to draw general conclusions for action, and none covered all staff groups working in the NHS.

The Nuffield Trust therefore convened a partnership of the key organisations with a stakeholding in the NHS to assess all available evidence in this area, and make recommendations for action. These stakeholding organisations are listed on page 11.

The stakeholding organisations formed themselves into the Partnership and agreed to commission an extensive literature survey by two doctors and a psychologist specialising in the area of occupational health. The results of the research have been agreed by The Partnership as academically sound, and the recommendations have been agreed by The Partnership as representing the most effective structural response to the problem of ill health among the NHS workforce.

The Partnership asked the Nuffield Trust, as an independent and objective commentator on the health sector, to present the findings and recommendations to Ministers, to put the report in the public domain, and to distribute it widely as the first step in responding to the challenge of improving ill health in the NHS workforce. The importance of addressing this challenge lies not only in the concern for the welfare of the staff of the NHS, but also in the implications for the quality of patient care.

John Wyn Owen CB
March 1998

SUBMISSION FROM THE PARTNERSHIP TO THE SECRETARY OF STATE FOR HEALTH

The Nuffield Trust has convened a Partnership (of leaders of bodies principally involved in the NHS) to assess the available evidence on the health of staff in the NHS and other health care workers, including general practitioners and their staff.

This paper from the Partnership invites Ministers:

(i) to join and lead the Partnership in developing effective action to remedy the situation disclosed by the research;

(ii) and to provide the keynote speaker for a conference to be held to start developing the programme of action.

We very much welcome the emphasis given in the White Paper *The New NHS* to the importance of establishing a new culture of partnership, openness and co-operation within the NHS, and we make this approach in that spirit. We find it encouraging that Chapter 6 of the White Paper, with its commitment to involving staff, sets out priorities which coincide with some of the areas for action identified by the research.

The Partnership has maintained a strict focus on scientifically rigorous research into ill health. This work was about the health of the workforce; it was not about morale or pay and conditions or the structure or management of the NHS unless there was research-based evidence of a link between such factors and ill health. Its purpose was to provide an objective basis for future action.

Although each individual piece of research is already in the public domain, few of the reports or scientific papers have attracted public attention or been acted upon. The effect of drawing them together in a single review is, however, pretty startling. The research shows, among other things, that worrying levels of psychological disturbance exist among hospital doctors and general practitioners at all stages in their career, and among nurses; that much of this ill health is associated with aspects of work; and that it can affect patient care. The cost implications for the NHS are also serious. There is less research on managers and other staff groups, but what there is suggests a comparable state of affairs.

The feeling within the Partnership is that, for the sake of good management and from simple compassion, both we and the Government should view these findings with due alarm, and accept shared responsibility for working quickly together to develop a programme for action. We are in no doubt as to our duty to publish and publicise the report. We should, however, try to ensure that it does not cause undue alarm to patients and the public.

The research covers not only the causes of ill health in the NHS but also interventions which have been found to be effective. The evidence on the latter is sparser than might be wished, but it does begin to show a way forward and we make a number of recommendations on the basis of it. We also make some recommendations based on experience and common sense. To take one example, the research provides evidence that the commitment in paragraph 6.31 of the White Paper that 'involving staff in service developments and planning change, with open communication and collaboration, is the best way for the NHS to improve patient care' is likely also to have a substantially beneficial effect on the health of the workforce. Management style clearly affects health. There is also little doubt that employers who are known to take good care of their workforce are also perceived as providing a good service to their customers.

The literature review was very thorough. It discovered gaps in the research which need to be addressed, but it could provide a benchmark against which to measure the effectiveness of an NHS-wide programme of action and the overall savings to the NHS which we believe would result. It might be helpful to bring the Audit Commission into the discussion at an early stage.

We consider that there should now be a process of consultation based on the report, and we propose to organise an early conference involving employers, purchasers and other groups, and the unions. The question which immediately arises is that of leadership. Every member of the Partnership has a stake in this issue. So does the Government. There are also other stakeholders who need to be drawn into the process. These very uncomfortable findings about the health of the NHS workforce will create challenges for each of us, but they will be much easier to handle and resolve if we can present a united and determined response to them.The Nuffield Trust brought together the Partnership and has provided impartial leadership, but the next stage must now be a matter for those responsible for the NHS workforce. Given the variety of employment patterns within the NHS, the danger is that we might lose the wider perspective we have just gained, and with it the impetus for urgent and effective action. The tone of the White Paper encourages us to hope that the Government will be willing to provide the leadership this problem needs. The Partnership believes that all those involved would respond with committed support.

The Partnership believes that its findings and recommendations are as applicable to Scotland, Wales and Northern Ireland, and the attention of the respective Secretaries of State is being drawn to this report.

MEMBERSHIP OF THE PARTNERSHIP

Mr John Wyn Owen,
Secretary, Nuffield Trust - convener

Mr Bob Abberley,
Head of Health, UNISON

Dr Thelma Bates,
Chairman of the Health Committee, General Medical Council

Professor Sydney Brandon,
Chairman, National Counselling Service for Sick Doctors

Ms Karen Caines,
Director, Institute of Health Services Management

Sir Kenneth Calman,
Chief Medical Officer, Department of Health

Mr Andrew Foster,
Chairman, Wigan and Leigh Health Services NHS Trust

Mr Stephen Griffin,
Director of Human Resources, St James's and Seacroft University Hospital Trust, Leeds

Miss Christine Hancock,
General Secretary, Royal College of Nursing

Dr Christopher Harling,
Dean, Faculty of Occupational Medicine

Lord Hunt,
formerly Chief Executive, NHS Confederation

Sir Donald Irvine,
President, General Medical Council

Dr Robert Kendell,
President, Royal College of Psychiatrists

Miss Catherine McLoughlin,
Co-Chair, NHS Confederation

Dr A W (Sandy) Macara,
Chairman of Council, British Medical Association

Dr Lotte Newman,
Past President, Royal College of General Practitioners

Mr Michael Scott,
Chief Executive, Derby City Hospital NHS Trust

Ms Jenny Simpson,
Chief Executive, British Association of Medical Managers

Ms Jean Trainor,
Deputy Chief Executive, NHS Confederation

Dame Mary Uprichard,
President of Council, United Kingdom Central Council for Nursing, Midwifery and Health Visiting

PROJECT TEAM

Dr Siân Williams,
Consultant in Occupational Medicine, Royal Free Hospital

Dr Susan Michie,
Senior Research Fellow in Health Psychology, UMDS

Dr Shriti Pattani,
Specialist Registrar in Occupational Medicine, Royal Free Hospital

ECONOMIC ADVISOR

Dr Peter West,
Senior Lecturer in Health Economics, UMDS

SECRETARIAT

Mr Max Lehmann
Deputy Secretary, Nuffield Trust

SUMMARY AND RECOMMENDATIONS

1 KEY MESSAGE

The new NHS White Papers emphasise the need for a healthy work force to achieve high quality patient care. This report identifies health problems in NHS staff, many of which are preventable and treatable. It also provides an evidence-based programme of action that should be implemented to:

- improve physical and psychological health
- improve work attendance
- improve organisational efficiency and effectiveness

2 A 10 POINT '*Action Now*' PLAN

The following 10 points are a comprehensive and integrated staff health improvement plan based on a review of the relevant scientific literature. The points are not put forward in order of priority (see table opposite).

3 ECONOMIC EVALUATION

Implementation of this staff health improvement plan should include a scientific evaluation of its effectiveness and the financial cost and benefit.

Recommendations	Responsibilities for action		
	Leadership	Guidance	Implementation
1. A major initiative to improve two way communications to increase staff involvement and enhance teamworking and control over work	Ministers	Government Taskforce (NHS White Paper)	Employers[1], professional andstaff organisations and individual staff
2. Evaluate work demands and review staffing	Ministers	NHSE[2], staff organisations and employers	Employers
3. Improve working environment and control violence to staff	Ministers	HSC/E[3]	Employers
4. Initiative to improve employment security	Ministers	NHSE, NHS Confederation and staff organisations	Employers
5. Family friendly policies to be available to staff throughout the NHS	Ministers	NHSE, NHS Confederation and staff organisations	Employers
6. Train managers to execute their responsibility to protect staff health	NHSE	NHSE	Employers
7. Facilitate and encourage staff to look after their health	NHSE	HEA[4], health promotion units, professional and staff organisations	Employers and individual staff
8. Occupational health services and confidential counselling services to be comprehensively available	Ministers	Faculty of Occupational Medicine and other specialist organisations	Employers
9. Manual handling policies for all i.e. training, assessment of risk and adequate equipment	NHSE	HSC/E	Employers
10. A publicity campaign to explain to everyone how all this fits together and their part in it	Ministers	The Partnership and NHSE	NHSE

1 Employers include Trusts, Health Authorities and General Practitioners
2 National Health Services Executive
3 Health and Safety Commission/Executive
4 Health Education Authority

TERMS OF REFERENCE

The objectives of The Partnership on the Health of the NHS Workforce were

1. To assess available evidence on morbidity among NHS staff and other healthcare workers, including general practitioners and their staff, and the extent to which this is generated by working in and for the NHS.
2. To consider recommendations already made for achieving improvements.
3. To establish what relevant work is in hand, and to identify gaps and any further commissions required.
4. To estimate the cost of avoidable work related ill health and other associated conditions.
5. To develop advice and a framework for courses of action for:
   - Government
   - the Department of Health and the Northern Ireland, Scottish and Welsh offices
   - the NHS Executive
   - all NHS employers, including GPs
   - professional organisations
   - registration authorities
   - organisations representing staff
6. To assist in meeting objectives as set out in NHS planning guidelines.
7. To develop benchmarks so that progress may be assessed.

1 AIMS

1.1 To develop an evidence-based programme of action to improve the health of the NHS workforce.

1.2. To describe ways in which this programme could be implemented, based on better use of existing resources and investment leading to future savings.

2 BACKGROUND

2.1 The problem of high levels of ill health in all groups of NHS staff has long been recognised. Recent figures from the CBI show that NHS staff have higher sickness absence than comparable staff groups in other sectors[1]. A recent large study shows that 27% of health care staff report high levels of psychological disturbance, compared with 18% of working people generally[2]. The nature of the work poses problems for both physical and psychological health, eg. the responsibility for people's lives, dealing with distressing illness and death. In addition the major organisational changes in recent years have affected all NHS staff, including GPs and other community staff, managers, professional groups and ancillary staff. Health problems have been found to vary geographically within the NHS suggesting the important role of local factors.

2.2 The levels of staff turnover and wastage are very high[3,4] and doctors are increasingly seeking early retirement[5,6]. This represents a loss of both skills and investment in training for all staff groups and the cost of training replacement staff drains much human and financial resources. With the current level of professional staff shortages, especially in medicine and nursing, the need to retain these highly trained staff is greater than ever.

2.3 Overwork is increasing both in hospital and community services. There are two elements to this overwork: the amount of work required of the individual in a given time and the excessive number of hours the individual is required to work. Shorter hospital stays mean faster throughput of patients; early discharge means sicker patients for general practitioners, practice staff and community services to care for in the community; closure of large psychiatric hospitals means more people requiring community care. Recent figures from the Department of Health show that over the last 10 years NHS activity has increased by 32% while expenditure has increased by only 16%. To bridge this gap there has been improved efficiency, but this has led to major pressures on staff.

2.4 An additional pressure for professional staff is the increased expectation and complaints by all patients and, at the extreme, litigation. These affect the behaviour of those fearing such action and have significant workload and health implications for those who are the subject of such complaints and litigation[7].

2.5 The HSE recently reported on the increasing violence and threats from patients and relatives[8]. In addition, isolation has become a great problem for some primary care staff and junior doctors.

2.6 The above factors contribute to ill health which undermines the quality and quantity of work and patient care[9]. Both the Government's new White Papers aimed at improving the NHS[10,11,12] and its Green Paper on improving public health[13] emphasise the importance of improving staff health and welfare. As a contribution to achieving this, the Nuffield Trust, on behalf of the Partnership on the Health of the NHS Workforce, commissioned this report. The Partnership represents most major organisations providing and regulating health care, and concerned with NHS staff health.

2.7 This report provides an evidence-based programme of action which should be implemented to improve physical and psychological health, work attendance and organisational efficiency and lead to long-term financial savings.

3 THE EVIDENCE BASE

The evidence (appendix 1) comprises a systematic literature review based on 131 papers selected from 5842 abstracts and 208 papers from other sources. Additional evidence was collected from 98 reports and 25 interviews with key individuals (appendix 2).

The following evidence is presented:

- the burden of ill health among NHS staff
- aspects of work associated with ill health
- evaluated interventions to improve staff health
- the economics of improving the health of the NHS workforce

3.1 The burden of ill health among NHS staff

Most research has concentrated on doctors and nurses, as reflected below. The limited research into other health care staff shows similar problems in other groups[14].

3.1.1 Doctors

- Studies found high levels of psychological disturbance[e] in 21% to 50% of hospital doctors and general practitioners (GPs) with all career grades being affected[2,15,16,17,18,19,20,21,22,23,24,25,26,27,28,29]. These levels are significantly higher than those for equivalent professional occupations[2,30]. In doctors, disturbance ranges from anxiety through emotional exhaustion[f] to clinical depression and suicide[19,20,31]. These problems have been found to be most severe for women doctors[2], especially those born overseas[31]. In some groups of doctors these problems are associated with unhealthy lifestyles (e.g. excessive alcohol consumption)[32,33] and with a lower standard of patient care[34]. Of doctors reporting that stress affected patient care, one in 10 said this led to a serious clinical mistake[34]. Anxiety and depression in GPs increased between 1987 and 1990[35].

e Psychological disturbance includes a variety of terms e.g. minor psychiatric disorder, emotional disturbance, psychological distress. The variation of terminology in the literature reflects both methods of measurement and researchers' preferences.

f Emotional exhaustion refers to one of the three dimensions measured by the Maslach Burnout Inventory.

Doctors report frequent minor illnesses and self prescription but most do not take time off work[21]. A third of junior doctors are not registered with a GP[21]. UK doctors show higher levels of work related stress and depression than US and Australian doctors[36].

3.1.2 *Nurses*

- High levels of psychological disturbance, ranging from emotional exhaustion to suicide[19], exist in 29% to 48% of nurses[2,37,38,39]. The level of psychological disturbance is significantly higher in nurses than in equivalent professional groups in the general population. Emotional exhaustion predicts sickness absence[40] and has doubled in community nurses between 1991 and 1995[37].
- Most nurses experience back pain at some time[41,42,43,44] which is associated with high absenteeism, staff turnover and ill health retirement[44,45]. This problem has increased by almost 40% from 1983 to 1995[41].

3.1.3 *Managers*

Between a third and a half of managers show high levels of psychological disturbance[2,26]. This is higher than for non-NHS managers, as high as for doctors, and women managers experience the highest levels[2].

3.1.4 *Professions allied to medicine*[g]

Psychological disturbance is at a high level in these groups (27%) and significantly higher than equivalent professions outside the NHS[2].

3.1.5 *Other staff groups*

Dentists show high levels of anxiety[46] and dentists and pharmacists show high levels of suicide[19] compared with the general population. Ambulance staff report more back pain than any other health service staff group[47].

g Professions allied to medicine (PAMs) include physiotherapists, chiropodists, dietitians, occupational therapists and orthoptists.

3.2 Aspects of work associated with ill health

There is evidence that work factors are not just associated with ill health but actually cause it[48]. Other work factors can protect people in vulnerable situations. For example having more control at work and greater social support enables greater tolerance of high workload.

3.2.1 All staff

A comparison across Trusts found that rates of psychological disturbance varied from 17-33%, with lower rates in Trusts characterised by smaller size, greater co-operation, better communication, more performance monitoring, a stronger emphasis on training and allowing staff more control and flexibility in their work[2]. High psychological disturbance has also been found among community staff, with work overload and lack of support contributing to this[49].

3.2.2 Doctors

- The overwhelming factors associated with psychological disturbance in doctors in junior to senior grades are the long hours worked[16,53,] the high workload and pressure of work[15,17,22,24,32,50,51,52,] and their effect on personal life[16,17,22,24,32,35]. Lack of role clarity has not been found to be a problem for these staff[54].

Additional factors associated with psychological disturbance are:

- In junior doctors, relationships with consultants and other staff[22,24,51] and making decisions; for women, sexual harassment at work, discrimination from senior doctors and lack of senior female role models[24].
- In consultants, low job satisfaction because of inadequate resources, feeling insufficiently trained in management skills and high levels of organisational responsibilities and conflict [17].
- In GPs, interruptions during and outside surgery hours and

patient demands[15,34,37].

- One in five psychiatrists retiring early cited work overload as the main reason[5].

3.2.3 Nurses

- The most frequently reported sources of psychological disturbance are high workload[37,39], workload pressures[38,55,56,57] and their effect on personal life[38], staff shortages, unpredictable staffing and scheduling and not enough time to provide emotional support to patients[55].
- Poor management style is associated with staff ill health[37] and predicts absenteeism[40,58]. Problems of management style include impatience, defensiveness, unsupportive leadership, lack of feedback and clarity and giving insufficient control[40,57].
- Distress in student nurses has been caused by low involvement in decision-making and use of skills and low social support at work[59].
- Management practices that lead to more open expression of views and joint problem solving result in reduced role conflict, ambiguity and stress[58].
- Low back pain is predicted by frequent manual handling of patients[43,44].

3.2.4 Other staff groups

There were few adequate UK studies describing the aspects of work associated with ill health for other occupational groups within the health service. European and US studies have dealt with many occupational groups in health care and the findings are broadly similar, so most of the following has been drawn from European and US studies.

3.2.4.1 Health care workers in Europe and the US

The key work factors associated with ill health are:

- work overload[60,61,62,63,64] and pressure of work[46,65,66,67]

- lack of control over work and lack of participation in decision making[61,68,69,70,71,72]
- poor social support at work[64,66,68,69,71,72,73,74,75,76,77]
- unclear management and work role[61,66,73,74,78,79]
- lifting, handling and uncomfortable postures[76,80,81,82]
- conflict between work and family demands[72,78,79]
- use of visual display units[80]

Health problems associated with the above are psychological disturbance (including depression and anxiety), cardiovascular mortality, back and joint pain and associated sickness absence.

3.2.4.2 Non health care workers in Europe and the US

The key work factors associated with illness in non-health care workers and of relevance to health care staff are:

- work overload and pressure [83,84,85,86,87,88,89,90,91,92,93,94,95,96,97,98,99,100,101]
- lack of control over work and lack of participation in decision making [69,83,88,90,91,92,94,95,97,98,100,101,102,103,104,105,106,107]
- monotonous work and not learning new skills[87,94,96,98,100,102,108]
- poor social support at work[69,97,102,105,107,109,110,111,112]
- unclear management and work role[88,91,99,109,113]
- lifting, handling and uncomfortable postures[85,100,107,108,112,114,115,116,117,118]
- conflict between work and family demands[88,119]
- interpersonal conflict[120,121,122]
- work reorganisation[106]

Health problems associated with the above are cardiovascular disease and mortality, psychological disturbance (including depression and anxiety), musculoskeletal pain, alcohol misuse, accidents, and associated sickness absence and medical retirement.

3.3 Evaluated Interventions

The researchers identified 13 interventions that were methodologically acceptable. Six were conducted with health care staff[123,124,125,126,127,128], four were randomised controlled trials [123,128,129,130] and two were conducted in the UK[131,132]. Seven were aimed at improving general physical and psychological problems[123,125,129,130,131,132,134] and six were aimed specifically at improving musculoskeletal problems[126,127,128,132,135,136].

The interventions aimed at improving general health were systemic organisational programmes supported by a mixture of staff and management training:

3.3.1 training skills to mobilise support at work and participate in problem solving and decision-making improved mental health, especially for those intending to leave[130]

3.3.2 support, advice and feedback from a psychologist reduced stress hormone levels[123]

3.3.3 communication skills training reduced staff resignations, sick leave, assaults and the costs of each of these[133]

3.3.4 teaching interpersonal awareness reduced emotional exhaustion and depression[134]

3.3.5 an organisational stress management programme led by senior management reduced medical malpractice claims and medication errors[125]

3.3.6 for physically inactive staff, exercise improved well being and reduced complaints of muscle pain[129]

3.3.7 an organisational intervention managing return to work after ill health, run by a local authority occupational health and human resource department, reduced sickness absence with considerable financial savings[131]

3.3.8 the majority of interventions aimed at reducing musculoskeletal problems consisted of prevention and early management by occupational health departments[126,127,132,135] or ergonomic intervention and skills training[137] and all of these were found to be cost effective by reducing injuries and absenteeism. Most of the adequate studies of training, isolated from an organisational intervention, have not demonstrated a benefit[128,136]

3.4 The economics of improving the health of the NHS workforce (appendix 3)

It is clear from the wide range of studies that have been carried out in the NHS that staff sickness is a major cost. The need to maintain staffing levels means that temporary replacement workers are much more likely to be used on the NHS than elsewhere, raising the costs of absence. Extrapolating estimates from individual studies to the current pay scales and staffing of the NHS (England) suggests that sickness absence rates of 5 percent or more are costing the NHS over £700 million a year. Clearly, not all this absence is preventable and we might wish staff with infectious diseases to make sure they stay away from vulnerable patients. But British industry overall averages around 3.7 per cent sickness absence. If the NHS could cut down sickness by only one percentage point, or about two and a half days per staff member per year, it could save itself over £140 million a year or the equivalent of one per cent of pay.

4. GAPS IN EVIDENCE BASE

Research findings are consistent with widespread beliefs about the health problems of NHS staff. This review has, however, highlighted important limitations in the research questions addressed and in the study designs used.

Studies of an acceptable methodological standard are required in the following areas:

- longitudinal studies that are able to investigate the causal relationships between work factors and health outcomes
- randomised control trials of interventions
- economic evaluation of interventions
- studies of staff groups other than doctors and nurses
- studies of the relationship between staff health and quality of patient care

5. PREVIOUS RECOMMENDATIONS FROM REPORTS

Of the 98 reports, 23 concern doctors, 9 concern nurses, 4 concern professions allied to medicine, 2 concern managers, 46 concern NHS staff in general and 14 concern employers in general. The overwhelming majority have been produced in 1996 and 1997.

5.1 Doctors

- increase staff and reduce hours of work and workload and allow for annual and study leave[138,139,140,141,142]
- better access to locum cover[140,143]
- review structure of work and devolve where appropriate[138,141]
- improve formal and informal support[138,140,141,144,145]
- develop teamwork[146]
- improve career guidance[141,143]
- increase flexible career structure and working patterns[138,142]
- provide counselling and stress management services[138,139,141,143,145,147,148,149]
- encourage/demand registration with GP[140,145,150]
- address self-prescribing[138,139,150]
- ensure adequate arrangements to identify and manage health problems including treatment out of area[145,149,151]
- enhance occupational health services[138,143,145,149,152]
- improve working environment e.g. doctors' accommodation[138,152]
- train in management skills[138,139,149], communication skills[140,141] and coping with stress [138,141,145] and alcohol and drug self awareness[138,140]
- train in skills to recognise and manage own health problems and those of colleagues[143]
- increase awareness among GPs of their responsibility for staff health and safety[153]

5.2 Nurses

- develop and implement anti-bullying policies[154]
- establish formal procedures for managing sickness absence[155]
- introduce family-friendly policies e.g. career-breaks and support personal development[3]
- national co-ordinator to evaluate back pain interventions[156]

5.3 Other health care staff

There were few reports restricted to other staff groups. Recommendations for health care staff in general include:

- involve staff in the management of health and safety and integrate health and safety management with all other aspects of management[157,158]
- improve employment policy and practice e.g. develop teamwork, better education and training, better management of sickness absence[140,146,159]
- clarify accountability and authority[147]
- ensure personal feedback, staff development plans and career guidance[4,147]
- increase flexible career structure and working patterns[4,147,160]
- stress management for managers and staff[141] and evaluation of stress management[161]
- provide accessible, effective and confidential occupational health services[157,162]
- train in management skills[4,139,163], communication skills[4], coping with stress and alcohol self-awareness[141]
- enhance human resource strategy and skills[164]
- ensure all NHS employers demonstrate progress towards best practice in health and safety and the health of the workforce[146,165,166,167]

- reduce the risk of violence at work by pro-active management, underpinned by positive commitment by senior managers and staff at all levels[8,168]

Progress in implementing these recommendations has been limited. The main barriers have been a lack of financial and human resources and a lack of will. The new White Papers[10,11,12] with their emphasis on quality should now lead to these issues being addressed.

5.4 Non health care staff

- involve staff in problem solving and decision-making[169]
- give staff control over their own work[170]
- effective communication with clear standards of performance, training needs and feedback part of appraisal[169,170]
- flexible hours[170]
- stress management at organisational and individual level[141,170]
- internal counselling service[141]

6. RECOMMENDATIONS

The following recommendations stem from the evidence uncovered in our literature review and an analysis of previous relevant reports. When planning this report, we did not set out to make the case for additional funding, but when assessing the literature it became clear that much ill health arises from workload, which is a resource issue. The literature also demonstrates that early investment can result in long term savings (see section 3.4). Some recommendations have minimal funding implications, others require allocation of existing health investment programmes differently and others require additional financial resources.

Many of the recommendations made in recent reports are consistent with our findings about the causes of ill health in the NHS and the interventions that are found to be effective. Examples are the Priorities and Planning Guidance for the NHS:1998/99[146,] Health Service Guidance[162] on Health and Safety, the Health Education Authority 'Health at Work in the NHS' project and most recently the new NHS White Papers[10,11,12].

Our recommendations are designed to be practical and achievable solutions, some in the short term and some requiring longer term planning. We suggest both the level at which they should be considered and the organisations to implement them. These include national policy makers, employers, regulators, statutory organisations responsible for registration, professional organisations and trade unions. The implementation of these recommendations will be facilitated by the representation of these organisations on the Partnership.

6.1. Management culture, style and skills

Our findings reveal the important influence of management style on staff health. The old competitive management culture has begun to change and must continue to do so. This will require action at all levels: leadership, commitment and investment from central government and the NHS Executive and from employers. For Trusts, commitment at board level is especially important since divisions and directorates may be semi-autonomous. Change will involve both training and support of managers and incorporation of specific objectives within organisational plans and senior staff appraisals.

6.1.1. Control over work and participation in decision-making

- enhance a sense of control by staff over the work environment. Increase their open expression of views and incorporate these into policies and practices
- encourage all staff, including clinicians, to participate in management, joint problem-solving and decision-making

6.1.2. Support and communication

- develop a culture in which staff are valued e.g. through induction programmes, regular positive feedback from managers, two way communication and early, sensitive addressing of problems
- give clear leadership and definitions to staff roles at work
- structure situations to promote both formal and informal social support within the workplace. Expand clinical supervision, mentorship, peer support and review for doctors, nurses and other professional staff, and team working for all staff
- support staff who are required to work long hours by consulting them on their needs and ensuring easy access to professional support out of hours

6.2 Employment practices

Employment practices to a large extent determine the organisational climate. Health care delivery is a very labour intensive activity, and the quality of this service is dependent on the quality of people management.

- evaluate work demands and review staffing
- maximise job security and minimise the use of short-term contracts
- follow the recommendations of the Working Time Directive[171]
- introduce more flexible employment practices e.g. allow staff to meet family commitments
- provide accessible career information and advice to all occupational groups including at student/training level
- ensure good career and staff development strategies
- ensure and act on policies to prevent bullying and harassment, including racial and sexual harassment
- implement policies on violence
- adopt risk management approach to staff health
- create an organisational climate in which working excessive hours is discouraged, with managers setting good examples
- encourage uptake of annual and study leave entitlement

6.3 Early detection and treatment of ill health and additional arrangements for prevention.

There is a statutory duty on employers to reduce illnesses and injuries caused by work. Hazard identification and risk assessment should be followed by clear arrangements to eliminate the risk, or if that is not possible, to reduce it as far as possible. This applies to all risks to health at work: physical, chemical, biological, ergonomic and organisational.

6.3.1 Psychological problems

In addition to the recommendations in section 6.1 and 6.2, all employers should provide all staff with counselling and stress management services that include organisational consultancy, preventative training and individual casework. Appropriately trained individuals should provide these services.

6.3.2 Musculoskeletal problems

- introduce policies to reduce musculoskeletal injuries e.g. minimal or no manual handling of patients and inanimate objects
- ensure adequate availability and use of specialised equipment to eliminate manual handling
- employers must comply with the Manual Handling Operations Regulations (1992)[172] through assessment of risk and the development of safe systems of work
- ensure best practice for treatment of back problems[173]

6.3.3 Alcohol and other drug misuse

Existing services for alcohol and other drug misuse (see 6.3.4) to coordinate efforts to:

- ensure that every employing authority has a well-publicised drug and alcohol policy, providing for the involvement of occupational health services, access to treatment and employment retention. Policies should be supportive, but should also state clear disciplinary procedures. The development of early and effective intervention should be a priority
- effect a cultural change in attitudes towards chemical dependence through education of students and staff
- publicise existing services more effectively to all staff
- inform staff of special arrangements for confidential advice during training and subsequent employment
- encourage a collaborative partnership between existing services, particularly in the sharing and monitoring of treatment outcomes

- encourage further research into comprehensive models of care incorporating intervention, treatment, support and monitoring as components of a dedicated scheme

6.3.4 *Treatment services*

- Some staff, such as doctors and nurses, may not wish to divulge medical problems to colleagues or may be concerned about the confidentiality of their casenotes. In addition to the choice of non-NHS services e.g. The National Counselling Service for Sick Doctors and the RCN Counselling Service, NHS care out of area should be available. Health Authorities and Trusts should develop collaborative arrangements for such staff. This choice must not impede the employers' obligation to ensure staff are well enough to work safely. It should be the duty of all employers to set up such arrangements as soon as possible and to promote them widely.

6.3.5 *Occupational Health Services*

- Promote the role of Occupational Health Services in the detection and assessment of physical and psychological health problems, the facilitation of appropriate care and rehabilitation back to work. Acknowledge that there are not at present enough specialists for all NHS staff to have access to a consultant led service using traditional models

To improve the quality of this service:

- implement a strategy to maximise the coverage of all health care organisations by high quality consultant occupational health doctors. To ensure that all services have access to an occupational health consultant, pilot schemes whereby consultants have a formal link to non-consultant services with a clear remit for training, supervision and support

- evaluate the effectiveness of different models of multi-disciplinary teams in their ability to detect and manage work-related ill health
- ensure the confidentiality of these services. Change the perception among staff where these services are perceived to lack confidentiality, using education strategies through student education, employers, the services themselves, professional and staff groups
- ensure policies for prevention and early management of important occupational risks such as 'needlestick' injuries and occupational allergies e.g. latex glove allergy

6.4 Special arrangements for doctors and other on-call staff

- provide good standards of food and clean, comfortable, quiet accommodation for those on-call overnight
- ensure better access to appropriately trained locum cover. This should not be the responsibility of the individual doctor but arranged via medical staffing
- review junior doctors' administrative, clerical and night work and promote multidisciplinary task sharing where appropriate
- initiate an educational campaign to discourage students and staff from seeking and giving inappropriate health care. Each locality should make special arrangements to facilitate GP registration, especially for junior doctors
- train health care professionals to assess and treat other professionals

All regions should set up a mechanism to review treatment services available for doctors locally. This could be done through the post-graduate deanery. There should be a well-advertised point of contact e.g. a named, senior, well-respected clinician, available to discuss the options open to the doctor and steer him or her towards an acceptable support system. This may be an out-of-area psychiatrist, surgeon, physician or occupational health consultant, an addiction treatment centre, or other appropriate service. These arrangements must be widely advertised so that doctors know how to access them.

6.5 Future research

NHS Research and Development should initiate and coordinate research into the health of NHS staff with other funding bodies such as HSE, MRC, Welcome Trust and Nuffield Trust. To overcome the gaps identified in section four, priority should be given to randomised controlled trials of interventions developed on the basis of previous research, to protocols with rigorous methodology and to studies of *all* staff groups.

7 IMPLEMENTATION AND MONITORING

The above recommendations should be drawn to the attention of all Boards of Trusts and Health Authorities who should be provided with the resources to ensure that these recommendations can be enacted or piloted.

7.1 Pilot schemes should be developed in selected Trusts or groups of general practices and should seek to identify and test changes in current NHS practices that would lead to staff health benefits. Each should be subject to external evaluation to assess its:

- effectiveness in improving the health of the NHS workforce
- revenue and manpower resource costs, short and long term, including benefits
- effect on the delivery of care

The process and outcome of planned changes need to be monitored by:

- improved routine collection of data about health indices eg. back problems, sickness absence. Partnership organisations will take responsibility for ensuring that this happens
- surveys to complement routine data collection

The pilot scheme leader should be a qualified researcher able to mount and conduct well designed evaluations. Proposals for these evaluations should be subject to scientific scrutiny. Their implementation should be overseen by a multidisciplinary body such as the National Institute of Clinical Excellence mentioned in the White Paper, reporting back to the Chief Medical Officers and the NHS Executive. Lessons that are learnt from properly evaluated schemes can then be applied more generally.

7.2 Partnership to re-convene in late 1998 to report on and assess the implementation of the report's recommendations, monitoring systems that have been initiated, and any data gathered.

CONCLUSION

The Partnership has considered the implications of these recommendations, and believes they can be incorporated within the following 10 point action plan, which provides a comprehensive and integrated staff health and improvement plan. The points are not put forward in order of priority.

Recommendations	Responsibilities for action		
	Leadership	Guidance	Implementation
1. A major initiative to improve two way communications to increase staff involvement and enhanced teamworking and control over work	Ministers	Government Taskforce (NHS White Paper)	Employers[1], professional andstaff organisations and individual staff
2. Evaluate work demands and review staffing	Ministers	NHSE[2], staff organisations and employers	Employers
3. Improve working environment and control violence to staff	Ministers	HSC/E[3]	Employers
4. Initiative to improve employment security	Ministers	NHSE, NHS Confederation and staff organisations	Employers
5. Family friendly policies to be available to staff throughout the NHS	Ministers	NHSE, NHS Confederation and staff organisations	Employers
6. Train managers to execute their responsibility to protect staff health	NHSE	NHSE	Employers
7. Facilitate and encourage staff to look after their health	NHSE	HEA[4], health promotion units, professional and staff organisations	Employers and individual staff
8. Occupational health services and confidential counselling services to be comprehensively available	Ministers	Faculty of Occupational Medicine and other specialist organisations	Employers
9. Manual handling policies for all i.e. training, assessment of risk and adequate equipment	NHSE	HSC/E	Employers
10. A publicity campaign to explain to everyone how all this fits together and their part in it	Ministers	The Partnership and NHSE	NHSE

1 Employers include Trusts, Health Authorities and General Practitioners
2 National Health Services Executive
3 Health and Safety Commission/Executive
4 Health Education Authority

REFERENCES

1 Managing absence: In sickness and in health. Confederation of British Industry, 1997.

2 Wall TD, Bolden RI, Borrill CS et al. Minor psychiatric disorder in NHS trust staff: occupational and gender differences. Br J Psychiatry 1997;171: 519-23.

3 Seccombe I, Smith G. Taking Part: Registered nurses and the labour market in 1997.The Institute for Employment Studies, 1997.

4 Finders Keepers: the management of staff turnover in NHS Trusts. Audit Commission bulletin, February 1997.

5 Kendell RE, Pearce A. Consultant psychiatrists who retired prematurely in 1995 and 1996. Psychiatr Bull 1997;21:741-45.

6 McBride M , Metcalfe D. General practitioners' low moral: reasons and solutions. Br J Gen Pract May 1995:227-229.

7 Ennis M, Grudzinskas G. The effect of accidents and litigation on doctors. In: Vincent C, Ennis M, Audley R (eds). Medical accidents. Oxford University Press, 1993.

8 Violence and Aggression to staff in the health services - guidance on assessment and management. London, HSE, 1997.

9 Firth-Cozens J. Stress, psychological problems and clinical performance. In: Vincent C, Ennis M, Audley R (eds). Medical accidents. Oxford University Press, 1993.

10 Secretary of State for Health. The new NHS. London: Stationery Office, 1997.

11 Secretary of State for Scotland. Designed to care: renewing the NHS in Scotland. London: Stationery Office, 1998

12 Secretary of State for Wales. NHS for Wales: Putting patients first. London: Stationery Office, 1998.

13 Secretary of State for Health. Our healthier nation. London: Stationery Office, 1998.

14 Prosser D, Johnson S, Kuipers E, et al. Mental health, 'burnout' and job satisfaction among hospital and community-based mental health staff. Br J Psychiatry 1996;169:334-337.

15 Sutherland VJ, Cooper CL. Identifying distress among general practitioners: predictors of psychological ill health and job dissatisfaction. Soc Sci Med 1993;37:575-581.

16 Chambers R, Campbell I. Anxiety and depression in general practitioners: associations with type of practice, fundholding, gender and other personal characteristics. Fam Prac 1996; 13:170-173.

17 Ramirez AJ, Graham J, Richards MA, et al. Burnout and psychiatric disorder among cancer clinicians. Br J Cancer 1995;71:1263-69.

18 Ramirez AJ, Graham J, Richards MA, et al. Mental health of hospital consultants: the effects of stress and satisfaction at work. Lancet 1996;347:724-28.

19 Charlton J. Trends and patterns in suicide in England and Wales. Int J Epidemiol 1995; 24 (Supp.1): S45-S51.

20 Carpenter LM, Swerdlow AJ, Fear NT. Mortality of doctors in different specialities:

findings from a cohort of 20 000 NHS hospital consultants. Occup Environ Med 1997;54:388-95.

21 Baldwin PJ, Dodd M, Wrate RM. Young doctors' health-II. Health and health behaviour. Soc Sci Med 1997;45:41-44.

22 Firth-Cozens J. Emotional distress in junior house officers. BMJ 1987;295:533-536.

23 Hale R, Hudson L. The Tavistock study of young doctors: report of the pilot phase. Br J of Hosp Med 1992;47:452-64.

24 Firth-Cozens J. Sources of stress in women junior house officers. BMJ 1990;301:89-91.

25 Guthrie EA, Black D, Shaw CM, et al. Embarking upon a medical career: psychological morbidity in first year medical students. Med Educ 1995;29:337-41.

26 Caplan RP. Stress, anxiety, and depression in hospital consultants, general practitioners, and senior health service managers. BMJ 1994; 309:1261-1263.

27 Blenkin H, Deary I, Sadler A, et al. Stress in NHS consultants. BMJ 1995;310:534.

28 Kirwin M, Armstrong D. Investigation of burnout in a sample of British general practitioners. Br J Gen Pract 1995;45:259-60.

29 Green A, Duthie HL, Young HL, et al. Stress in surgeons. Br J Surg 1990;77:1154-8.

30 Grainger C, Harries E, Temple J, et al. Job satisfaction and health of house officers in the West Midlands. Health Trends 1995; 27:27-31.

31 Richings JC, Khara GS, McDowell. Suicide in young doctors. Br J Psychiatry 1986;149:475-478.

32 Chambers R, Wall D, Campbell I. Stresses, coping mechanisms and job satisfaction in general practitioner registrars. Br J Gen Pract 1996;46:343-8.

33 Working Group on the Misuse of Alcohol and Other Drugs by Doctors. The misuse of alcohol and other drugs by doctors. London: British Medical Association, 1998.

34 Firth-Cozens J, Greenhalgh, J. Doctors' perceptions of the links between stress and lowered clinical care. Soc Sci Med 1997;44:1017-22.

35 Sutherland VJ, Cooper CL. Job stress, satisfaction, and mental health among general practitioners before and after introduction of new contract. BMJ 1992;304:1545-8.

36 Whitley TW, Allison Jr EJ, Gallery ME, et al. Work-related stress and depression among practicing emergency physicians: an international study. Ann Emerg Med 1994;23:1068-71.

37 Fagin L, Brown D, Bartlett H, et al. The Claybury community psychiatric nurse stress study: is it more stressful to work in hospital or the community? J Adv Nurs 1995;22:347-358.

38 Tyler P, Cushway D. Stress, coping and mental well-being in hospital nurses. Stress Medicine 1992;8:91-8.

39 Tyler PA, Carroll D, Cunningham SE. Stress and well-being in nurses: a comparison of the public and private sectors. Int J Nurs Stud 1991;28:125-30.

40 Firth H, Britton P. 'Burnout', absence and turnover amongst British nursing staff. J Occup Psychol 1989;62:55-59.

41 Leighton DJ, Reilly T. Epidemiological aspects of back pain: the incidence and prevalence of back pain in nurses compared to the general population. Occup Med 1995;45:263-7.

42 Pheasant S, Stubbs D. Back pain in nurses: epidemiology and risk assessment. Appl Ergonomics 1992;23:226-232.

43 Smedley J, Egger P, Cooper C, Coggon D. Prospective cohort study of predictors of incident low back pain in nurses. BMJ 1997;314:1225-8.

44 Smedley J, Egger P, Cooper C, et al. Manual handling activities and risk of low back pain in nurses. Occup Environ Med 1995;52:160-3.

45 Heap DC. Low back injuries in nursing staff. J Soc Occup Med 1987;37:66-70.

46 Cooper CL, Watts J, Baglioni Jr AJ, et al. Occupational stress amongst general practice dentists. J Occup Psychol 1988;61:163-174.

47 Turnbull N, Dornan J, Fletcher B, et al. Prevalence of spinal pain among the staff of a district health authority. Occup. Med 1992;42:143-8.

48 Frese M. Stress at work and psychosomatic complaints: a causal interpretation. J Appl Psychol 1985;70:314-28.

49 Prosser D, Johnson S, Kuipers E, et al. Perceived sources of work stress and satisfaction among hospital and community mental health staff, and their relation to mental health, burnout and job satisfaction. J Psychosom Res 1997;43:51-59.

50 Agius RM, Blenkin H, Deary IJ, et al. Survey of perceived stress and work demands of consultant doctors. Occup Environ Med 1996;53:217-224.

51 Williams S, Dale J, Glucksman E, et al. Senior house officers' work related stressors, psychological distress, and confidence in performing clinical tasks in accident and emergency: a questionnaire study. BMJ 1997;314:713-8.

52 Deary IJ, Blenkin H, Agius RM, et al. Models of job-related stress and personal achievement among consultant doctors. Br J Psychol 1996;87:3-29.

53 Baldwin PJ, Dodd M, Wrate RW. Young doctors' health-I. How do working conditions affect attitudes, health and performance Soc Sci Med 1997;45:35-40.

54 Heyworth J, Whitley TW, Allison Jr EJ, et al. Correlates of work-related stress amongst consultants and senior registrars in accident and emergency medicine. Arch Emerg Med 1993;10:279-88.

55 Plant ML, Plant MA, Foster J. Stress, alcohol, tobacco and illicit drug use amongst nurses: a Scottish study. J Adv Nurs 1992;17:1057-67.

56 Baglioni Jr AJ, Cooper CL, Hingley P. Job stress, mental health and job satisfaction among UK senior nurses. Stress Medicine 1990;6:9-20.

57 Landeweerd JA, Boumans NPG. The effect of work dimensions and need for autonomy on nurses' work satisfaction and health. J Occup Organ Psychol 1994;67:207-217.

58 Gray-Toft PA, Anderson JG. Organisational stress in the hospital: development of a model for diagnosis and prediction. Health Serv Res 1985;19:753-74.

59 Parkes KR. Occupational stress among student nurses: a natural experiment. J Appl Psychol 1982;67:784-796.

60 Niedhammer I, Lert F, Marne MJ. Back pain and associated factors in French nurses. Int Arch Occup Environ Health 1994;66:349-57.

61 Arsenault A, Dolan SL, Van Ameringen MR. Stress and mental strain in hospital work: exploring the relationship beyond personality. J Organisational Behav 1991;12:483-493.

62 Lehto TU, Helenius HYM, Alaranta HT. Musculoskeletal symptoms of dentists assessed by a multidisciplinary approach. Community Dent Oral Epidemiol 1991;19:38-44.

63 Rundcrantz B, Johnsson B, Moritz U, et al. Occupational cervico-brachial disorders among dentists. Scand J Soc Med 1991;19:174-80.

64 Marshall NL, Barnett RC. Work-related support among women in caregiving occupations. J Community Psychol 1992; 20:36-42.

65 Bru E, Mykletun RJ, Svebak S. Work-related stress and musculoskeletal pain among female hospital staff. Work and Stress 1996;10:309-321.

66 Martin TN. Role stress and inability to leave as predictors of mental health. Human Relations 1984;37:969-983.

67 Estryn-Behar M, Kaminski M, Peigne E, et al. Stress at work and mental health status among female hospital workers. Br J Indust Med 1990;47:20-28.

68 Johnson JV, Hall EM, Ford DE, et al. The psychosocial work environment of physicians. J Occup Environ Med 1995; 37(9):1151-9.

69 Johnson JV, Stewart W, Hall EM, et al. Long-term psychosocial work environment and cardiovascular mortality among Swedish men. Am J Public Health 1996;86:324-31.

70 Petterson IL, Arnetz BB, Arnetz JE. Predictors of job satisfaction and job influence: results from a national sample of Swedish nurses. Psychother Psychosom 1995;64:9-19.

71 Miller KI, Ellis BH, Zook EG, et al. An integrated model of communication, stress, and burnout in the workplace. Communication Research 1990;17:300-26.

72 Thomas LT, Ganster DC. Impact of family-supportive work variables on work-family conflict and strain: a control perspective. J Appl Psychol 1995;80:6-15.

73 Revicki DA, Whitley TW, Gallery ME. Organisational characteristics, perceived work stress, and depression in emergency medicine residents. Behav Med 1993;19:74-81.

74 Revicki DA, May HJ. Organisational characteristics, occupational stress, and mental health in nurses. Behav Med 1989;15:30-6.

75 Parker PA, Kulik JA. Burnout, self- and supervisor-rated job performance, and absenteeism among nurses. J Behav Med 1995;18:581-99.

76 Linton SJ. Risk factors for neck and back pain in a working population in Sweden. Work & Stress 1990;4:41-9.

77 Linton SJ, Kamwendo K. Risk factors in the psychosocial work environment for neck and shoulder pain in secretaries. J Occ Med 1989;31:609-13.

78 Brooke PP, Price JL. The determinants of employees absenteeism: an empirical test of a causal model. J Occup Psychol 1989;62:1-19.

79 Rees D, Cooper CL. Occupational stress in health service workers in the UK. Stress Medicine 1992;8:79-90.

80 Steffy BD, Jones JW. The psychological impact of visual display terminals on employees' well-being. Am J Health Promotion 1989;4:101-7.

81 Troussier B, Lamalle Y, Charruel C, et al. Socioeconomic impact and prognostic factors of low back pain subsequent to a work-related injury among Grenoble teaching hospital employees. Rev. Rhum 1993; 60:112-9.

82 Hagberg M, Wegman D. Prevalence rates and odds ratios of shoulder-neck diseases in different occupational groups. Br J Indust Med 1987;44:602-610.

83 Siegrist J, Peter R. Threat to occupational status control and cardiovascular risk. Isr J Med Sci 1996;32:179-84.

84 Noor NM. Work and family roles in relation to women's well-being: a longitudinal study. Br J Soc Psychol 1995;34:87-106.

85 Sobti A, Cooper C, Inskip H, et al. Occupational physical activity and long-term risk of musculoskeletal symptoms: a national survey of post office pensions. Am J Ind Med 1997;32:76-83.

86 Bergenudd H, Nilsson B. The prevalence of locomotor complaints in middle age and their relationship to health and socioeconomic factors. Clin Orthop 1994;308:264-270.

87 Houtman ILD, Bongers PM, Smulders PGW, et al. Psychosocial stressors at work and musculoskeletal problems. Scand J Work Environ Health 1994;20:139-45.

88 Reifman A, Biernat M, Lang EL. Stress, social support, and health in married professional women with small children. Psychology of Women Quarterly 1991; 15:431-45.

89 Carayon P, Yang C, Lim S. Examining the relationship between job design and worker strain over time in a sample of office workers. Ergonomics 1995;38:1199-211.

90 Crum RM, Muntaner C, Eaton WW, et al. Occupational stress and the risk of alcohol abuse and dependence. Alcohol Clin Exp Res 1995;19:647-655.

91 Frone MR, Russell M, Cooper ML. Job stressors, job involvement and employee health: a test of identity theory. J Occup Organisational Psychol 1995;68:1-11.

92 Landsbergis PA, Schnall PL, Warren K, et al. Association between ambulatory blood pressure and alternative formulations of job strain. Scand J Work Environ Health 1994;20: 349-63.

93 Everson SA, Lynch JW, Chesney MA, et al. Interaction of workplace demands and cardiovascular reactivity in progression of carotid atherosclerosis: population based study. BMJ 1997;314:553-8

94 Haan MN. Job strain and ischaemic heart disease: an epidemiologic study of metal workers. Ann Clin Res 1988;20:143-5.

95 Karasek RA, Theorell T, Schwartz JE, et al. Job characteristics in relation to the prevalence of myocardial infarction in the USA health examination survey (HES) and the health and nutrition examination survey (HANES). Am J Public Health 1988;78:910-8.

96 Alfredsson L, Spetz C, Theorell T. Type of occupation and near-future hospitalisation for myocardial infarction and some other diagnoses. Int J Epidemiol 1985;14:378-88.

97 Johnson JV, Hall EM. Job strain, work place social support, and cardiovascular disease: a cross-sectional study of a random sample of the Swedish working population. Am J Public Health 1988;78:1336-42.

98 Karasek Jr RA. Job demands, job decision latitude, and mental strain: implications for job redesign. Administrative Science Quarterly 1979;24:285-311.

99 Bacharach SB, Bamberger P, Conley S. Work-home conflict among nurses and engineers: mediating the impact of role stress on burnout and satisfaction at work. J Organisational behav 1991;12:39-53.

100 Alfredsson L, Karasek R, Theorell T. Myocardial infarction risk and psychosocial work environment: an analysis of the male Swedish working force. Soc Sci Med 1982;16:463-7.

101 Payne R, Fletcher BC. Job demands, supports, and constraints as predictors of psychological strain among schoolteachers. J Vocational Behav 1983;22:136-147.

102 Stansfeld SA, North FM, White I, et al. Work characteristics and psychiatric disorder in civil servants in London. J Epidemiol Community Health 1995;49:48-53.

103 Rubenowitz S, Norrgren F, Tannenbaum, AS. Some social psychological effects of direct and indirect participation in ten Swedish companies. Organisation Studies 1983; 4:243-59.

104 Shannon HS, Walters V, Lewchuk W, et al. Workplace organisational correlates of lost-time accident rates in manufacturing. Am J Ind Med 1996;29:258-68.

105 Driscoll RJ, Worthington KA, Hurrell Jr JJ. Workplace assault: an emerging job stressor. Consulting Psychol J: Practice and Research 1995;47:205-212.

106 Karasek R. Lower health risk with increased job control among white collar workers. J Organisational Behav 1990; 11:171-185.

107 Theorell T, Harms-Ringdall K, Ahlberg-Hulten G, et al. Psychosocial job factors and symptoms from the locomotor system: multicausal analysis. Scand J Rehab Med 1991; 23:165-173.

108 Svensson HO, Anderssson GBJ. Low-back pain in 40- to 47-year-old men: work history and work environment factors. Spine 1983;8:272-276.

109 Fusilier MR, Ganster DC, Mayes BT. Effects of social support, role stress, and locus of control on health. J Management 1987;13:517-28.

110 Singh RG. Relationship between occupational stress and social support in flight nurses. Aviat Space Environ. Med. 1990;61:349-52.

111 LaRocco JM, House JS, French Jr JRP. Social support, occupational stress, and health. J Health Soc Behav 1980;21:202-18.

112 Linton SJ. Risk factors for neck and back pain in a working population in Sweden. Work and Stress 1990;4:41-9.

113 Smith KK, Kaminstein DS, Makadok RJ. The health of the corporate body: illness and Organisational dynamics. J Appl Behav Sci 1995;31:328-51.

114 Tuomi K, Luostarinen T, Ilmarinen J, et al. Work load and individual factors affecting work disability among aging municipal employees. Scand J Work Environ Health 1991;17:94-8.

115 Holmstrom EB, Lindell J, Moritz U. Low back and neck/shoulder pain in construction workers: occupational workload and psychosocial risk factors. Spine 1992;17:663-71.

116 Bergenudd H, Nilsson BO. Back pain in middle age; occupational workload and psychological factors: an epidemiologic survey. Spine 1988:58-60.

117 Bergenudd H, Lindgarde F, Nilsson BO, et al. Shoulder pain in middle age: a study of prevalence and relation to occupational work load and psychosocial factors. Clin Orthop 1988;231:234-238.

118 Heliovaara M. Occupation and risk of herniated lumbar intervertebral disc or sciatica leading to hospitalisation. J Chron Dis 1987;40:259-64.

119 Marshall NL, Barnett RC. Family-friendly workplaces, work- family interface, and worker health. In: Job stress in a changing workforce. Washington DC. Keita GP, Hurrell JJ. American Psychological Associations, 1994.

120 Romanov K, Appelberg K, Honkasalo M, et al. Recent interpersonal conflict at work and psychiatric morbidity: a prospective study of 15,530 employees aged 24-64. J Psychosom Res 1996;40:169-76.

121 Appelberg K, Romanov K, Heikkila K, et al. Interpersonal conflict as a predictor of work disability: a follow-up study of 15,348 Finnish employees. J Psychosom Res 1996;40:157-67.

122 Falger PRJ, Schouten EGW. Exhaustion, psychological stressors in the work environment, and acute myocardial infarction in adult men. J Psychosom Res 1992; 36:777-86.

123 Lokk J, Arnetz B. Psychophysiological concomitants of organisational change in health care personnel: effects of a controlled intervention study. Psychother Psychosom 1997;66:74-7.

124 Katz P, Kirkland FR. Violence and social structure on mental hospital wards. Psychiatry 1990;53:262-77.

125 Jones JW, Barge BN, Steffy BD, et al. Stress and medical malpractice: organisational risk assessment and intervention. J Appl Psychol 1988;73:727-735.

126 Haig AJ, Linton P, McIntosh M, et al. Aggressive early medical management by a specialist in physical medicine and rehabilitation: effect on lost time due to injuries in

hospital employees. J Occup Med 1990;32:241-4.

127 McGrail MP, Tsai SP, Bernacki EJ. A comprehensive initiative to manage the incidence and cost of occupational injury and illness. J Occup Environ Med 1995;37:1263-8.

128 Donaldson CS, Stanger, LM, Donaldson MW, et al. A randomised crossover investigation of a back pain and disability prevention program: possible mechanisms of change. J Occup Rehabilitation 1993;3:83-94.

129 Gronningsaeter H, Hytten K, Skauli G, et al. Improved health and coping by physical exercise or cognitive behavioural stress management training in a work environment. Psychology and Health 1992;7:147-63.

130 Heaney CA, Price RH, Refferty J. Increasing coping resources at work: a field experiment to increase social support, improve work team functioning, and enhance employee mental health. J Organisational behav 1995;16:335-52.

131 Malcolm RM, Harrison J, Forster H. Effects of changing the pattern of sickness absence referrals in a local authority. Occup Med 1993;43:211-5.

132 Ratti N, Pilling K. Back pain in the workplace. Br J Rhematol 1997;36:260-4.

133 Smoot SL, Gonzales JL. Cost-effective communication skills training for state hospital employees. Psychiatr Serv 1995;46:819-22.

134 Kagan NI, Kagan H, Watson MG. Stress reduction in the workplace: the effectiveness of psychoeducational programs. J Counselling Psychol 1995; 42:71-8.

135 Wiesel SW, Boden SD, Feffer HL. A quality-based protocol for management of musculoskeletal injuries. Clin Orthop 1994;301:164-76.

136 van Poppel MNM, Koes BW, Smid T, et al. A systematic review of controlled clinical trials on the prevention of back pain in industry. Occup Environ Med 1997;54:841-7.

137 Crocker KS. Reducing back pain sickness absence. Occupational Health Review October1991:8-10.

138 British Medical Association. Stress and the medical profession. London: BMA, 1992.

139 Firth-Cozens J. Stress in Doctors: a longitudinal study. Report to the NHS Executive R&D Division, 1995.

140 Baldwin PJ, Dodd M, Wrate RW. Young doctors: work, health and welfare, 1997.

141 Firth-Cozens J. Stress in health professionals: report on current research. Report to the NHS Executive R&D Division, 1997.

142 Medical workforce standing advisory committee: third report. Planning the medical workforce. Department of Health, 1997.

143 McKevitt C, Morgan M, Simpson J, et al. Doctors' health and needs for services. London: Nuffield Provincial Hospitals Trust, 1996.

144 McKevitt C, Morgan M, Holland WW. Protecting and promoting doctors' health: the

work environment and counselling services in three sites. London: Nuffield Provincial Hospitals Trust, 1996.

145 Silvester S, Allen H, Withey C, et al. The provision of medical services to sick doctors: a conspiracy of friendliness? London: Nuffield Provincial Hospitals Trust, 1994.

146 NHS Executive. Priorities and planning guidance for the NHS: 1998/99. NHSE, 1997.

147 Healthy work patterns project final report. S & W Region NHS, 1997.

148 Ogden J, Hopkins R. GP-Care. A 3 part evaluation of a new counselling service for GPs and their families. Dovedale Counselling Ltd, 1997.

149 Chambers R, Maxwell R. Database of activities and initiatives in the UK associated with reducing GPs' stress or improving GPs' well-being. Royal College of General Practitioners, London, 1997.

150 Good medical practice. 1995. London: General Medical Council.

151 Chemical dependence in the medical profession: A report from the medical ethics committee. British Medical Association 1997.

152 Nuffield Provincial Hospitals Trust. Taking care of doctors' health. London: Nuffield Provincial Hospitals Trust, 1996.

153 Chambers R, George V, McNeill A, et al. Survey of general practices: Health at work in primary care research study (draft). Health Education Authority, London 1997.

154 Alderman C, Cox CN. Bullying in the workplace. Nursing Standard. 1997;11:22-26.

155 Seccombe I, Buchan J. Absent nurses: the costs and consequences. Institute of Manpower Studies, 1993.

156 Back pain in nurses: summary and recommendations. The Robens Institute, University of Surrey, 1984.

157 Management of health and safety in the health services. London: HSE, 1994.

158 Health and safety briefing pack no. 1 stress at work. The Chartered Society of Physiotherapy, 1997.

159 Measuring and monitoring sickness absence: A practical guide. HEA, 1995.

160 Caines K, Hammond V. Creative career paths in the NHS: The agenda for action. Institute of Health Service Management, 1996.

161 Cox T. Stress research and stress management: putting theory to work. HSE contract research report no.61/1993. London: HSE.

162 NHS Health and Safety Issues HSG(97)6. NHSE 1997.

163 Report on two pilot training courses carried out by the Industrial Society, for Health at Work in the NHS. HEA 1997.

164 Deegan M. Managing human resources in the NHS - a service wide approach (executive letter). Leeds: NHS Executive, 1997.

165 Health and safety in NHS acute hospital trusts in England. National Audit Office, 1996.

166 Health and safety inspection in the health services (internal document). Health Services Advisory Committee 1997.

167 Spinal pain survey. The Chartered Society of Physiotherapy. 1994.

168 Health and safety briefing pack no. 2 violence at work. The Chartered Society of Physiotherapy, 1997.

169 Employee motivation and the psychological contract. Institute of Personnel and Development, 1997.

170 Managing best practice: Managing stress. The Industrial Society, 1995.

171 HSG(97)6 Working Time Directive (93/104/EC). OJ L314, Dec 1993.

172 Manual Handling Operations Regulations (1992). London: HMSO 1992.

173 Waddell G, Feder G, Mackintosh I, Lewis A, Lewis M. Clinical guidelines for the management of acute back pain. Royal College of General Practitioners, 1996.

174 Understanding systematic reviews of research on effectiveness, CDR report 4.NHS centre for reviews and dissemination, the University of York, 1996.

175 Seccombe I. Measuring and monitoring sickness absence from work. Institute of Employment Studies report. 1995.

176 Health at work in the NHS: key indicators report. The Institute for Employment Studies, Health Education Authority 1994.

177 Trusting in the future: towards an audit agenda for NHS providers. The Audit Commission, Stationery Office, London, 1994.

178 Making the case for health at work in the NHS, briefing pack. Health Education Authority 1997.

APPENDIX 1:

SYSTEMATIC LITERATURE REVIEW METHODOLOGY

The method used was based on the Cochrane systematic literature review methodology[174], with the following stages;

1. GATHERING THE DATA

The three electronic databases used were Medline (1987-1997), Psychinfo (1987-1997) and Bids (1991-1997). The search strategy was of MeSH key words in each of the three categories: work factors; staff; and health[a] or organisational outcomes. Language was restricted to English. This generated 3606 abstracts from Medline, 912 from Bids and 1324 from Psychinfo, totalling 5842 abstracts from which 362 papers were selected using the criteria described below. In addition 185 papers were found through scanning reference lists and 23 were accessed through researchers and professionals in the field, giving a total of 570. Grey literature including reports, booklets and discussion papers was gathered from interviewees and other contacts. These were all classed as reports for the purpose of this review.

2. INITIAL SELECTION CRITERIA

Abstracts were divided into three 3 categories: descriptions, associations and interventions. For the descriptions, only abstracts of UK health care staff were included. For the associations, developed countries and all types of employment were included. Dissertations were excluded, as were studies of very specific staff groups or settings and health promotion activities based in workplaces. The latter is a large literature and is of more relevance to public health than occupational health. All abstracts were selected independently by two researchers, with an inter-rater agreement of 80-90%. Disagreements were resolved by discussion.

Health outcomes included physical and psychological measures, including physiological measures of stress and excluding perceived stress.

3. INFORMATION EXTRACTION

Information extraction sheets were developed that included:

- study aim
- type of study population e.g. occupational group
- demographic characteristics
- main health and organisational outcomes
- sampling strategy, sample size and response rate
- type of study measure
- study design
- type of intervention
- summary of the results

4. FURTHER SELECTION CRITERIA

Coded papers were excluded from the review if the studies included;

- volunteer or inadequately described sample
- a response rate of less than 60%
- no standardised measures

On this basis 439 papers were excluded, leaving 131 papers in the review.

APPENDIX 2:

INTERVIEW SCHEDULE

1. Does your organisation take a view on how to improve the health of your members/staff?

2. What are you as a member of the Partnership currently doing in support of the Partnership?

3. Are you aware of any articles or reports that would help our research into:

   - The association between working in the NHS and ill health
   - The evaluation of interventions aimed at improving the health of NHS staff
   - Previous recommendations aimed at improving health
   - Reasons for non-implementation or failure of previous recommendations

4. Are you aware of any current work addressing the above?

5. Do you know of previous attempts to improve the health of NHS staff? If so, what happened?

6. Which areas do you consider the most important for interventions?

7. What do you consider to be the main gaps in our knowledge in these areas?

8. Are there specific research projects that you would like to see commissioned and what would you do with the results?

9. What do you think have been the main barriers to translating recommendations and research findings into policies and practice?

10. What steps should be taken to maximise the chances that any of the recommendations that this project makes will be implemented?

11. Are there any other individuals that you think we should talk to or organisations that we should contact?

12. Are you aware of the recommendations of the recent Nuffield Trust report 'Taking Care of Doctors' Health' and the Sheffield Institute of Work Psychology report 'Mental Health of the Workforce in NHS Trusts'?

13. What changes have you or your organisation made as a result of them?

14. What are the reasons for not implementing their recommendations?

15. How would you suggest funding the investment needed to make the necessary changes happen? Do you know of any examples of good practice which have achieved this?

16. Assuming the recommendations are actioned, what mechanisms would be best to monitor implementation: how would they be carried out and by whom?

INTERVIEWEES

Thelma Bates	Chairman of the Health Committee, General Medical Council
Sydney Brandon	Chairman, National Counselling Service for Sick Doctors
Karen Caines	Director, The Institute of Health Services Management
Sir Kenneth Calman	Chief Medical Officer, Department of Health
Ruth Chambers	Stress Fellow, Royal College of General Practitioners
Cary Cooper	Professor of Organisational Psychology, UMIST
Derek Day	Director of Corporate Affairs, NHS Confederation
Malcolm Forsythe	Professorial Fellow in Public Health, University of Kent
Andrew Foster	Chairman, Wigan and Leigh Health Services NHS Trust
Virginia George	Manager of the 'Health at Work in the NHS' project, Health Education Authority
Phil Gifford	Principal Inspector and leader of the Health Services National Interest Group, HSE
Richard Griffin	Co-director of Industrial Relations, the Chartered Society of Physiotherapy
Gillian Hardy	Clinical Psychologist, The University of Sheffield

Christopher Harling	Dean, Faculty of Occupational Medicine
Philip (now Lord) Hunt	formerly Chief Executive, NHS Confederation
Jane Huntley	Programme Manager, Work Health project, Health Education Authority
Robert Kendell	President, Royal College of Psychiatrists
Roger Kline	National Secretary (Health), MSF
Caroline Langridge	Fellow, Kings Fund
Catherine McLoughlin	Co-Chair, NHS Confederation
Myfanwy Morgan	Reader in sociology of Health, UMDS
William O'Neill	Science and Research Advisor, BMA
Anne Marie Rafferty	Director of Centre for Policy in Nursing Research, London School of Hygiene and Tropical Medicine
Jon Richards	Research Officer, Health Service, UNISON
Jenny Simpson	Chief Executive, British Association of Medical Managers
Claire Sullivan	Health and Safety Officer, the Chartered Society of Physiotherapy
Suzanne Tyler	Deputy Director, The Institute of Health Services Management
Michael Wilks	Chair of the BMA Ethics Committee

INDIVIDUALS CONSULTED

Pamela Baldwin	Senior Researcher, Well at Work Research Institute, Edinburgh
Gwyn Bevan	Economist, London School of Economics
Tom Cox	Professor of Organisational Psychology, University of Nottingham
Elaine Fazel	Moving and Handling Co-ordinator, Wigan and Leigh Health Services NHS Trust
Jenny Firth-Cozens	Principal Research Fellow, University of Leeds
David Guest	Professor of Organisational Psychology, Birkbeck College, London
Sue Parkin-Smith	Health and Safety Inspector, Health Services National Interest Group, HSE
Ian Seccombe	Senior Research Fellow, Institute for Employment Studies
Grace Owen	General Secretary, National Association for Staff Support within the health care services

APPENDIX 3

Peter West
Senior Lecturer in Health Economics,
Department of Public Health Medicine, UMDS

THE COSTS OF ILL HEALTH AMONG NHS WORKERS

This section draws together a range of estimates of the cost of ill health among NHS workers.

Estimates are drawn from a range of studies, with different methodologies and undertaken at different times, and may not be wholly comparable, one with another. They are also static estimates of the direct impact of ill health among NHS workers. But the NHS workforce is a dynamic one, responding over time to changes in pay and working conditions. For example, sickness absence may be keeping some nurses in the profession by creating a demand for part time agency and bank nurses.

COST ESTIMATES FOR ILL HEALTH IN THE NHS WORKFORCE

Estimates are summarised here with the year of data collection and total costs. Where estimates have been grossed up to give an estimate for the NHS as a whole, sources typically relate to England and have been grossed up to the NHS workforce in England.

Sickness Absence

The main costs of sickness absence are listed by[175]:

DIRECT COSTS:	INDIRECT COSTS:
• occupational sick pay • statutory sick pay • temporary cover • additional overtime costs • lost production or service provision	• management time • administrative and clerical time • interrupted work flow • lower productivity of temporary staff (and of staff working when unwell) • reduced quality and costs of lost materials • added costs of meeting slipped deadlines • occupational health provision • reduced morale

Additional costs in the NHS include the possible loss of longer-term employment opportunities of other kinds for staff sick or injured in the NHS and the cost of training additional staff to replace those leaving the NHS workforce. (In practice, the cost of training also depends on the balance between pay and productivity over a nursing career and there may be advantages to the NHS in training more nurses who are more productive, relative to their pay scales, in the early years of their career.)

Lower productivity due to illness includes not only slower working when sick or by temporary replacement workers but also potential harm to patients and lower quality care.

COST ESTIMATES OF SICKNESS ABSENCE/INJURY AMONG NHS STAFF

Estimates from a range of published studies have been grossed up to the NHS (England) workforce as reported in the most recent published data and adjusted for inflation since the studies' year of data collection. The source study is noted.

SICKNESS ABSENCE:

- Sickness among nurses: £90.5 million per year, England[155]
- Sickness among all NHS staff: £714 million per year, England[176]
- Back injuries: cost of £73.5 million per year and replacement staff costs of £52.5 million per year, England[177]
- Accidents: £12.34 million per year, England[165]
- Accident compensation for staff and patients: £30.4 million, England[165]
- Accident-related early retirements: £71 million, England[165]

HARM TO PATIENTS

Some studies[34], report patients deaths and other serious mistakes in care due to stress among doctors. No estimates of the costs of this have been identified.

In the US[125] one study has shown a relationship between medical malpractice claims in clinical areas and the levels of stress (though this could be casual, from malpractice to stress, due to fear of being sued, rather than the reverse, with stress contributing to errors).

COST EFFECTIVENESS OF INTERVENTIONS

A number of studies have been summarised[178] but these include US studies in which a wide range of activities are carried out by health work programmes. Estimates of impact include reductions of 9-29 per cent in absence and 4 per cent rise in productivity, equivalent to £64 - £200 million for NHS, England.

Manual handling intervention[178] at Wigan and Leigh (1993) reduced total hours lost in all activities by 31.5 per cent and hours lost through handling patients by 84 per cent, equivalent to £62 million per year savings on loss of work time and £44 million per year replacement costs for NHS, England.

STAFFING LEVELS AND STAFF STRESS

A number of studies suggest that doctors take too little sick leave, partly due to problems of obtaining locums, and that staffing levels generally may be generating staff stress and lead to sickness absence in nurses and other staff. Hiring additional staff may be a beneficial strategy for patient care but will not be cost-saving for doctors since, by definition, the aim is to increase their sickness absence. For other staff, an increase in staff could generate a reduction in sick leave, raising staff levels further. More staff would increase costs but a part of the cost (but probably not all of it) would be offset by reduced costs of sickness cover. To be cost saving, a very large percentage reduction in sickness absence would have to be achieved by adding a relatively small number of staff to the establishment.

ACKNOWLEDGMENTS

We are deeply grateful to:
Susan Adams and Pauline Summers from the Royal Free Hospital School of Medicine library and Angela Gunn from UMDS library;

Rita Doudakian and Dr Ioana Kennedy from the Royal Free Hospital Occupational Health and Safety Unit for their help in checking the manuscript;

Deborah Matthews from the Royal Free Hospital Occupational Health and Safety Unit for her time and persistance in developing the layout of the manuscript;

Dr Olwen Williams, Consultant in clinical effectiveness, ACET, Cambridge, for all her help in summarising the reports.